A. Wilson.

For Raul L. S.

BLACKIE CHILDREN'S BOOKS

Published by the Penguin Group
Penguin Books Ltd, 27 Wrights Lane, London W8 5TZ, England
Penguin Books USA Inc., 375 Hudson Street, New York, New York 10014, USA
Penguin Books Australia Ltd, Ringwood, Victoria, Australia
Penguin Books Canada Ltd, 10 Alcorn Avenue, Toronto, Ontario, Canada M4V 3B2
Penguin Books (NZ) Ltd, 182-190 Wairau Road, Auckland 10, New Zealand

Penguin Books Ltd, Registered Offices: Harmondsworth, Middlesex, England

First published in hardback by Blackie Children's Books 1989
This paperback edition first published 1993
10 9 8 7 6 5 4 3 2 1

Printed in Hong Kong by Imago

A CIP catalogue record for this book is available from the British Library

ISBN 0–216–94039–7

The Streetwise Kid.

Lorraine Simeon
and
Sarah-Jane Stewart

Blackie Children's Books

In this book there is a message, it is there to make you see
The streets are a dangerous place for any child to be.

Some children on the streets alone like to think they're big
But the best way to think is like a Streetwise Kid.

Never wander far from home when you go out to play:
Don't go anywhere, with anyone, no matter what they say.

If someone tries to force you, don't be frightened to say 'No'.
Always tell your parents where you intend to go.

Never play with footballs in the middle of the street.
Don't take anything from strangers—money, games or sweets.

Should a stranger try to tempt you with a very cunning fib
Be sensible and act like a Streetwise Kid.

Never play with older children,
whom you do not know.
Never do what they say,
just because they tell you so.
Any child who copies others
is always sorry that they did.
The best way to think
is like a Streetwise Kid.

Never lose control when you are walking down the road.
Remember, learn and always use your streetwise safety code.

If you see someone you know, never dash across the street;
You'll look stupid if you get knocked down, and end up at their feet.

DANGER
KEEP
OUT!

All those kids who play in gangs,
and run around with sticks and stones
They do silly things with others
they wouldn't dare to do alone,
Like hide and seek on building
sites, and places where men work,
In disused factories and railway lines
where they could get hurt.

If you want to be a Streetwise Kid, it's not too late to learn
Because danger lies in wait around each corner that you turn.

For a silly boy, a greedy girl, a child who fails to see
How dangerous and deadly the streets can really be.

So be sensible, be clever, and above all you must be strong.
Don't be taken in by anyone, or made to do what's wrong.

This is something to remember, and keep firmly in your mind:
The Streetwise Kid survival kit, the best one of its kind.